Pages 2–3

Pages 22–23

Pages 18–19

Pages 26–27

Pages 28-29

Pages 38-39

Pages 34-35

Pages 46-47

Pages 40-41

Pages 4-5

Pages 6-7

Pages 8-9

Pages 10-11

Pages 12-13

Pages 14-15

Pages 16-17

Pages 16–17

Pages 20–21

Pages 24–25

Pages 30–31

Pages 36–37

Pages 32–33

Pages 42–43

Page 48

Pages 44–45

Published by Hinkler Books Pty Ltd
45–55 Fairchild Street
Heatherton Victoria 3202 Australia
www.hinkler.com

hinkler

© Hinkler Books Pty Ltd 2018

Packaged by Collaborate Agency

ISBN: 978 1 4889 3659 3

Printed and bound in China

CONTENTS

BRILLIANT INSECTS AND BUGS

Bugs may be small, or even microscopic, but they are by far the largest group of animals on Earth. There are over a million species and they are everywhere. Some bugs have beautiful markings, some are ingeniously clever and some can even kill humans!

The scale and variety of bugs make them some of the animal kingdom's most fascinating creatures. Take a tour of their amazing, tiny world and find out:

✷ Which bug has the most painful sting?

✷ Which bug carries up to 50 babies on its back?

✷ Which bug has poisonous fangs that can penetrate leather?

✷ Which bug spreads sleeping sickness?

✷ Which bug can stay inside your body for up to 25 years?

Match the glow-in-the-dark stickers to the bug silhouettes.

TYPES OF INSECT AND BUG

The first thing to know about bugs is that they can be divided into five main groups:

1. Insects   2. Arachnids   3. Centipedes   4. Worms   5. Molluscs

Let's take a look at what defines each group.

INSECTS

You can immediately spot an insect as it has six legs and its body is divided into three parts. Most insects also have wings. Insects include beetles, butterflies, moths, bees, wasps, ants, flies, dragonflies, grasshoppers and stick insects.

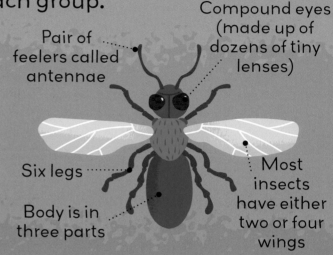

Pair of feelers called antennae

Compound eyes (made up of dozens of tiny lenses)

Six legs

Body is in three parts

Most insects have either two or four wings

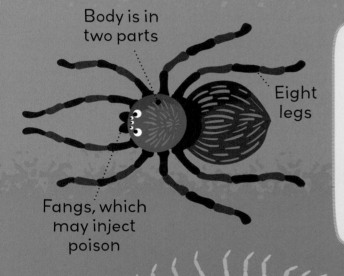

Body is in two parts

Eight legs

Fangs, which may inject poison

ARACHNIDS

Spiders and scorpions are arachnids as they have eight legs and their bodies are divided into two parts. Unlike spiders, scorpions have a pair of claws as well. There are over 35,000 types of spider and it's hard to escape them as they are found all over the world, except for very cold or mountainous regions.

Head

Segmented trunk

Each trunk has a pair of legs

CENTIPEDES

These worm-like bugs are made up of a head and a trunk. The trunk is divided into many segments. Each segment has a pair of legs and is protected by a hard, external skeleton. Millipedes are similar to centipedes except they have two pairs of legs on each segment of their trunk.

Soft, segmented body

WORMS

There are nearly 3000 different kinds of worms! The most well-known is the earthworm. Worms all have long, soft bodies but no legs. Although they don't have eyes, they can tell when they are in the dark or in the light as they can sense light through their skin. And although they have no ears, their bodies can sense the vibrations when things are moving nearby.

Head with a mouth but no eyes

Spiral shell that the snail can hide in for protection

Soft body

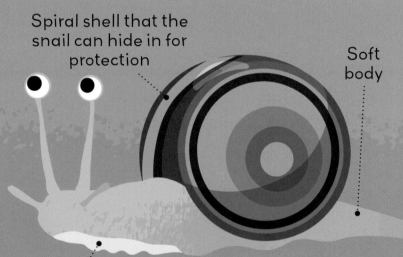

MOLLUSCS

These soft-bodied bugs include snails and slugs. They have no legs but they can move by means of a muscular 'foot' on their underside.

Single muscular 'foot' for moving along

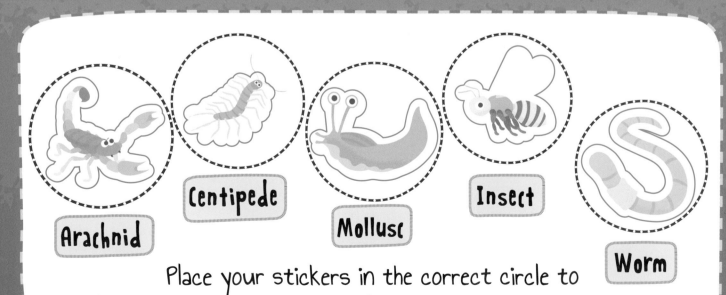

Arachnid

Centipede

Mollusc

Insect

Worm

Place your stickers in the correct circle to show that you know your bugs.

BEETLES

Nearly half of all the insects in the world are beetles; in fact, there are a staggering 300,000 different beetle species. It's no surprise that they vary hugely in appearance and can be found in all temperatures, from scorching deserts to freezing ice caps. While some beetles cause damage by eating crops, others help the planet by pollinating flowers and eating harmful insects.

IS IT A BEETLE?

Most insects have four wings, but it is the beetle's hardened front wings that distinguish it from other insects. These wings are often glossy and brightly coloured and provide a protective cover for the body. The beetle has a second pair of wings at the rear that it uses for flying.

LADYBIRD

Found: Worldwide

Length: Up to 18 mm (0.7 in)

Feeds on: Tiny insects like aphids

Fun fact:
The dome-shaped ladybird uses its bright colours as a defensive warning to predators. When threatened, it secretes an oily, yellow fluid that tastes disgusting.

HORNED DUNGBEETLE

Found: Worldwide

Length: Up to 3 cm (1.2 in)

Feeds on: Dung

Fun fact:
It can push a ball of animal poo hundreds of times its body weight – the equivalent of you lifting about six double-decker buses.

JEWELLED FROG BEETLE

Found: South-east Asia

Length: 3 cm (1.25 in)

Feeds on: Leaves

Fun fact:
This beetle has a small head, large frog-like hind legs and metallic wings that glint like a reddish jewel.

Match the stickers to the bug silhouettes.

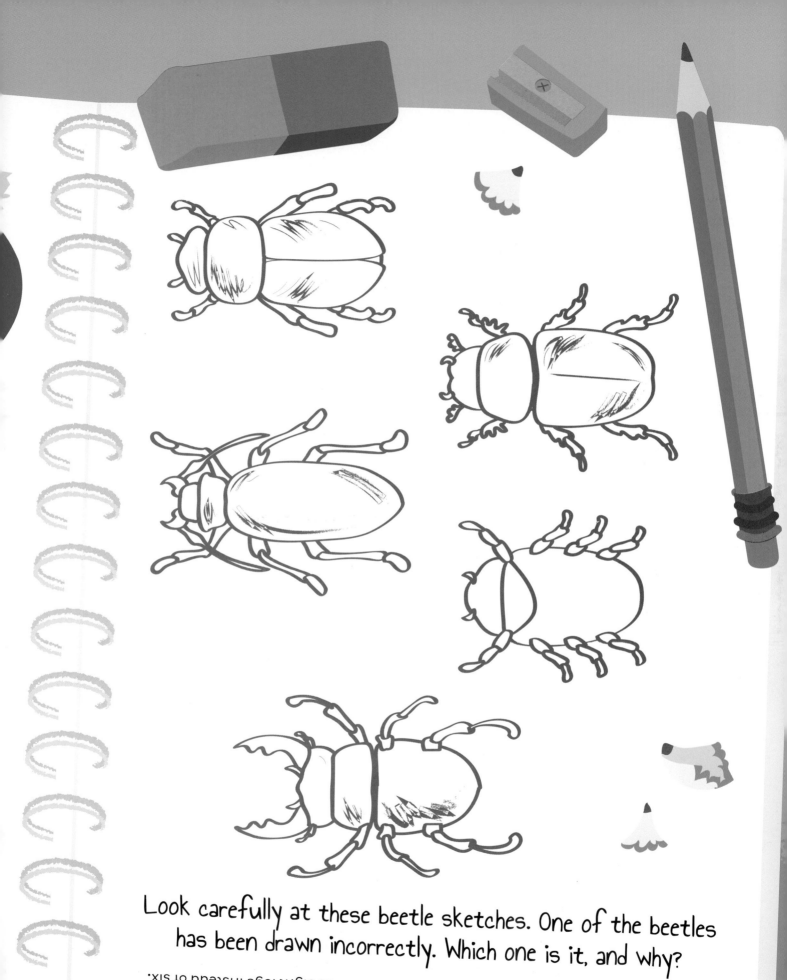

Look carefully at these beetle sketches. One of the beetles has been drawn incorrectly. Which one is it, and why?

BUTTERFLIES AND MOTHS

With their delicate wings and stunning colours, butterflies are often considered the most beautiful of all insects. There are about 17,500 species of butterflies in the world and they vary in size from the blue pygmy in California, with a wingspan of 1.3 cm (0.5 in), to Papua New Guinea's Queen Alexandra's birdwing, whose wingspan is 28 cm (11 in).

BUTTERFLY FACTS

✺ Throughout the world, butterflies can be found in gardens, grasslands and forests, and even in the Arctic tundra.

✺ Monarch butterflies can travel 3000–5000 km (2000–3000 mi) each year in search of warmer climates.

✺ A long feeding tube (proboscis) allows a butterfly to suck up nectar from deep within flowers.

✺ A butterfly uses its antennae to smell and to keep balanced.

✺ To warm its wings before it can fly, a butterfly sits in the sun.

Match the stickers to the bug silhouettes.

ULYSSES BUTTERFLY

Found: Australia

Wingspan: 14 cm (5.5 in)

Feeds on: Flowers, tree blossom

Fun fact:
This butterfly has striking blue wings that can be seen from hundreds of metres away.

GLASS WING BUTTERFLY

Found: South America

Wingspan: 3 cm (1.2 in)

Feeds on: Flower nectar

Fun fact:
Its unique see-through wings allow this butterfly to blend in with its surroundings so that predators can't easily see it.

MOTH FACTS

- Like the butterfly, the moth has four wings but they are much duller in colour. Moths also have thicker, hairier bodies than butterflies. It is thought that this is to keep them warm after dark.

- Moths are most active after dark, feeding on the nectar of flowers that bloom at night. They fly using the moon and stars to navigate.

- Moths must vigorously vibrate their wings to warm them up before they can fly.

EMPEROR MOTH

Found: Europe, Northern Asia

Wingspan: 6 cm (2.6 in)

Feeds on: Heather and other plants

Fun fact:
This colourful moth has black 'eye-spots' on its wings.

GARDEN TIGER MOTH

Found: USA, Europe

Wingspan: 6.5 cm (2.6 in)

Feeds on: Plants, flowers

Fun fact:
The distinctive wing pattern of this moth acts as a warning to predators as its body fluids are poisonous.

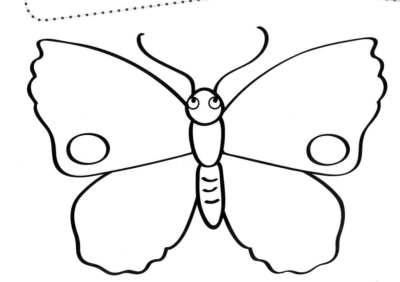

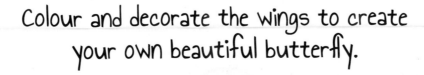

Colour and decorate the wings to create your own beautiful butterfly.

BEES AND WASPS

Bees and wasps are often confused with each other. Both types of insect have a very narrow waist and both can give a painful sting! But there are important differences: bees have hairy, round bodies while wasps have smooth, slender bodies. Wasps are also a lot more aggressive than bees.

ABOUT BEES

The best-known bees are the honeybee and the bumblebee, but there are over 20,000 species of bee. Most are very social insects, living in large groups (colonies) of up to 50,000 bees! We usually think of bees living in a hive, but a hive is a man-made home for honeybees. Most bee colonies live in nests. Bees are vegetarian, feeding on nectar from flowers. Honeybees convert this nectar to honey, storing it in honeycombs that they make from wax.

DID YOU KNOW?

A wasp can sting repeatedly but many bees can only sting once, as the bee's stinger is ripped out when it is used.

A wasp's nest

A honeybee making honeycomb inside its nest

This honeybee wants to get to the hive's exit. Help it find the route it needs to take to get through the honeycomb.

START

EXIT

ABOUT WASPS

Not all wasps are yellow and black — some species are bright red and some are even metallic blue. Wasps are carnivores that feed on other insects. Some types of wasp are social, like bees, but others live on their own.

ANTS AND TERMITES

Ants, like bees and wasps, are very social insects, living in colonies of up to a million ants! Ants are known for their bite. Many species of ant inject an acid with their bite, which can make the bite site feel just as painful as a bee or wasp sting. Termites are a different type of insect to ants but they look very similar, and they also live in large colonies.

Match the stickers to the bug silhouettes.

BLACK GARDEN ANT

Found: Worldwide

Length: Up to 0.7 cm (0.28 in)

Feeds on: Nectar, small insects, fruit

Fun fact:
These are the world's most common species of ant. Although the male black ant only survives a few weeks, the female can live for 15 years.

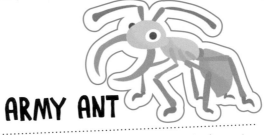

ARMY ANT

Found: South American rainforests

Length: 1.2 cm (0.5 in)

Feeds on: Insects, worms, even birds and small animals

Fun fact:
Army ants march like soldiers in huge numbers making it possible to overpower prey more than one hundred times their own size. They tear the prey apart with their pincers and dissolve them in acid.

BULLET ANT

Found: South America

Length: 3 cm (1.2 in)

Feeds on: Nectar and small insects

Fun fact:
Bullet ants get their name from their bite, which is so painful, it feels like being shot by a bullet. No other insect's bite or sting hurts more.

WHITE TERMITE

Found: Worldwide

Length: 1.5 cm (0.6 in)

Feeds on: Dead plant material

Fun fact:
Termites, though not true ants, are often referred to as 'white ants' as they look pale when they haven't eaten anything for a while. There are over 3000 different species.

The common black ant loves sugary foods. Which unlucky ant won't find a sugary treat at the end of its trail?

FLIES AND DRAGUNFLIES

Which is the yuckiest species of insect? A lot of people would vote for flies. Many species of fly feed or lay their eggs on rotting food, dung and dead animals. Some, like the mosquito and the midge, feed on blood. Their gross feeding habits spread many serious diseases. In contrast, dragonflies can help reduce disease, as they feed on mosquitoes and horseflies and often live in areas where these flies thrive. The shimmering colours and the agile flight of the dragonfly make it one of the world's most admired creatures.

FLY FACTS

- ✺ Flies range in size from tiny 0.5 mm midges to bluebottles and mosquitoes that can be up to 19 mm long.

- ✺ They have a single pair of wings and tiny structures behind these wings help flies keep their balance in flight.

- ✺ Hundreds of miniscule lenses in their eyes give flies good eyesight. Tiny claws and pads on their feet also make them very good climbers.

BLUEBOTTLE

Found: Most parts of the world

Length: 1.2 cm (0.5 in)

Feeds on: Decaying meat, including dead bodies

Fun fact:
The bluebottle takes its name from its bright blue metallic colour.

TSETSE FLY

Found: Mid-Africa

Length: 1.4 cm (0.5 in)

Feeds on: Blood of animals, using its blade-like mouthparts.

Fun fact:
The tsetse fly spreads deadly diseases like sleeping sickness, which kills up to 300,000 people each year.

DRAGONFLY FACTS

✵ Dragonflies are found throughout the world and have been around for over 300 million years!

✵ When migrating, the globe skimmer dragonfly travels further than any other insect – 17,703 km (11,000 mi) across the Indian Ocean and back!

FLAME SKIMMER DRAGONFLY

Found: America

Length: 7.6 cm (3 in)

Feeds on: Ants, flies, moths

Fun fact:
This bright red dragonfly scares off predators by suddenly darting at them.

SOUTHERN HAWKER DRAGONFLY

Found: Europe

Length: 7 cm (2.7 in)

Feeds on: Various small flying insects.

Fun fact:
This nimble dragonfly can reach speeds of up to 30 km/h (19 mph).

PLAINS CLUBTAIL DRAGONFLY

Found: USA, Canada

Length: 6 cm (2.5 in)

Feeds on: Flying insects

Fun fact:
This common dragonfly takes its name from a bump near the tip of its body that looks like a club.

Match the stickers to the bug silhouettes.

GRASSHOPPERS AND STICK INSECTS

The grasshopper is fascinating because of its amazing jumping ability. Its long, slender, green body also enables it to blend in well with its grassy or leafy surroundings. The stick insect and its close relative, the leaf insect, are even better at this. When clinging to a twig or leaf, they can be almost impossible to see.

SWEET MUSIC

Grasshoppers rub their back legs against their wings to create a chirping sound. This 'song' helps them to communicate with other grasshoppers and can also attract a mate. Each species has its own special song. Crickets are very similar to grasshoppers, but they make their song by rubbing their wings together. While grasshoppers can be heard during the day, crickets usually only appear in the evening.

STRIPE WINGED GRASSHOPPER

Found: Europe, Asia

Length: Up to 2 cm (0.8 in)

Feeds on: Grasses and plants

Fun fact:
This agile creature has one of the quietest of all grasshopper songs.

Use your stickers to complete the pictures on this page.

FOAMING GRASSHOPPER

Found: South Africa

Length: Up to 8 cm (3.1 in)

Feeds on: Various plants

Fun fact:
This dangerous grasshopper releases a toxic foam when attacked.

ABOUT STICK AND LEAF INSECTS

These insects remain perfectly still when a predator approaches, so they look just like the stick or leaf they are perched on. Their green or brown colour helps to disguise them, as does their shape. Stick insects have long, slim bodies, while leaf insects are wider and flatter.

STICK INSECT

Found: Worldwide, particularly in the tropics

Length: 2.9 cm (1.15 in)

Feeds on: Leaves of shrubs

Fun fact:
Stick insects have fake buds and leaf scars as part of their camouflage.

WALKING LEAF

Found: Australia, south-east Asia

Length: 5 cm (2 in)

Feeds on: Plants

Fun fact:
One of the best camouflaged creatures in the animal world. Females have markings that resemble leaf veins, and some species even have disease spots and holes, making it impossible to distinguish them from the leaf they are sitting on.

Can you spot the 10 leaf and stick insects in the picture?

SPIDERS

These eight-legged creatures are probably the easiest to recognise of all bugs. While some are deadly poisonous, others, including many big, hairy spiders, are harmless. Most spiders build a web to catch their prey, but some use an ambush technique.

BRAZILIAN WANDERING SPIDER

Found: South America

Leg span:
Up to 15 cm (6 in)

Feeds on: Tree frogs, lizards, mice

Fun fact:
Instead of building webs, this spider wanders the jungle floor at night, looking for prey. As one of the most dangerous spiders, its venom can kill humans.

BLACK WIDOW SPIDER

Found: North America

Leg span:
Up to 3.8 cm (1.5 in)

Feeds on: Insects

Fun fact:
This poisonous spider has a red hourglass shape on its underside. It gets its name from the fact that the female often eats its mating partner.

ZEBRA BACK SPIDER

Found: Europe, North America

Leg span:
Up to 1 cm (0.4 in)

Fun fact:
Rather than building a web to catch its prey, this spider lies in wait and then pounces.

REDBACK SPIDER

Found: Australia

Leg span:
Up to 1 cm (0.4 in)

Feeds on: Crickets, small lizards

Fun fact:
This is a very venomous spider that can kill a human. It likes hiding in mailboxes, sheds and under toilet seats, so beware!

EIGHT-SPOTTED CRAB SPIDER

Found: South-east Asia

Leg span:
Up to 2.5 cm (1 in)

Feeds on: Butterflies, bees

Fun fact:
Straight out of Halloween, this endangered, bright yellow spider has eight black spots.

HUNTSMAN SPIDER

....

Found: Australia, Africa,
Asia

Leg span:
Up to 30 cm (12 in)

Feeds on: Small reptiles,
insects

Fun fact:
This giant, hairy spider has
crab-like legs and chases
after prey with a fast,
jumping run.

OGRE-FACED SPIDER

....

Found: Australia, Africa,
South America

Leg span:
Up to 7.6 cm (3 in)

Feeds on: Other spiders,
insects

Fun fact:
With two huge, ogre-like
eyes, this scary creature
can detect its prey's
slightest movement in
almost total darkness.

Use your
glow-in-the-dark stickers
to complete the
creepy-crawly scene.

DADDY LONG LEGS

....

Found: Worldwide

Leg span:
Up to 5 cm (2 in)

Feeds on: Other spiders,
insects

Fun fact:
Easily recognised by its
extremely long, skinny
legs, this spider makes
a thin, tangled web to
catch its prey.

FLOWER
CRAB SPIDER

....

Found: Worldwide

Leg span:
Up to 3 cm (1.2 in)

Feeds on:
Butterflies, bees

Fun fact:
This tiny spider waits on a
flower and then scuttles
sideways like a crab,
ambushing its prey.

TARANTULA

....

Found: Africa, Australia,
South America

Leg span:
Up to 30 cm (12 in)

Feeds on: Mice, birds

Fun fact:
A large, hairy spider that
sinks its fangs into its prey.
It wards off predators by
raising its front legs as
a warning.

SCORPIONS

Scorpions are closely related to spiders but with much thinner, more brittle bodies. They also have between six and twelve eyes, distinctive claw-like pincers and a venomous tail. The scorpion combines its pincers and tail to become a lethal killing machine, able to overpower much bigger animals like snakes and rodents. Some species of scorpion are so venomous that they can even kill people.

DEFENCE AND ATTACK

Scorpions use their venomous tails for both defence and attack. If a predator approaches, a scorpion will make a hissing sound by rubbing its tail along its back as a defensive warning. If this doesn't work, it will quickly attack. If the prey is small, the scorpion simply holds it between its pincers, liquefies its body with special juices, then eats it! For larger prey, the scorpion will arch its poisonous tail over its back to sting and paralyse the heart and lungs of its victim.

COMMON EUROPEAN SCORPION

Found: Europe, North Africa

Length: Up to 4 cm (1.5 in)

Feeds on: Small animals, insects

Fun fact:
It is a largely harmless scorpion whose sting is just like a bee sting to humans.

YELLOW THICK-TAILED SCORPION

Found: Sahara Desert in Africa

Length: Up to 10 cm (4 in)

Feeds on: Insects

Fun fact:
One of the most dangerous scorpions, it is very aggressive and has a deadly venom, causing several human deaths each year.

AFRICAN ROCK SCORPION

Found: South Africa

Length: Up to 10 cm (4 in)

Feeds on: Insects

Fun fact:
This scorpion is larger than most, with a flatter body that allows it to squeeze between narrow cracks in rocks.

DEATHSTALKER SCORPION

Found: North Africa

Length: Up to 8 cm (3 in)

Feeds on: Crickets, spiders

Fun fact:
This deadly scorpion is particularly dangerous to humans. Not only does its plastic appearance make it look like a harmless toy, but it uses its stinger to lash out like a whip at surprising speed.

SCORPION SECRETS!

- Scorpions mainly come out at night. During the day, they hide in their burrows and under rocks.

- Special bristles on their legs and pincers enable scorpions to scamper across sand without sinking. They can climb almost any type of surface – even if they're upside down.

- A scorpion's pincers aren't only used for nasty things! During mating, the male uses them to embrace the female and 'dance' with her.

- Unlike most bugs and insects, scorpions do not lay eggs. They give birth to live young – as many as 100 at a time. The mother scorpion carries all the babies on her back until they are old enough to look after themselves.

Add the stickers to the missing scorpions. Then make another scorpion appear on the rock by joining the dots.

WURMS AND CENTIPEDES

These are the bugs that wriggle and slither across the ground, living in the soil and in decomposed leaves on the forest floor. While worms have no legs at all, centipedes sometimes have hundreds!

TYPES OF WORM

Add the correct glow-in-the-dark worm stickers!

Segmented worms	Segmented worms live in the soil. They have soft bodies divided into a series of circular muscles. They move by squeezing together, then relaxing, these muscles.	
Round worms	Round worms, or thread worms, live in the soil or within decaying matter on the forest floor. Many are microscopic but some can be as long as 1 m (39 in).	
Tapeworms	Tapeworms have flat, ribbon-like bodies and live inside animals and humans. They are parasites, which means they live in or on another living thing and depend on that living thing for food and shelter.	

GIPPSLAND EARTHWORM

Found: Australia

Length: Up to 2 m (80 in)

Feeds on: Clay soil

Fun fact:
This giant earthworm has as many as 400 body segments.

GREEN PADDLE WORM

Found: Worldwide

Length: Up to 25 cm (10 in)

Feeds on: Oil, moist sand and water

Fun fact:
Tiny bristles and paddle-like attachments on each of its body segments enable this worm to move across rocks and swim in water.

CENTIPEDES

✸ Centipedes have 15 or more brittle body segments, each with a single pair of legs. Centipedes range from just a few millimetres in length to over 30 cm (12 in). Some species have over 350 legs!

✸ Centipedes are carnivorous and move quickly to hunt down prey, and use poisonous fangs contained in their front pair of legs to attack.

✸ Millipedes are similar to centipedes but have two pairs of legs on each body segment. They feed on vegetable matter rather than live prey, and so do not move as quickly as centipedes. They defend themselves by curling up into a tight ball.

Circle the six differences between these two leaves.

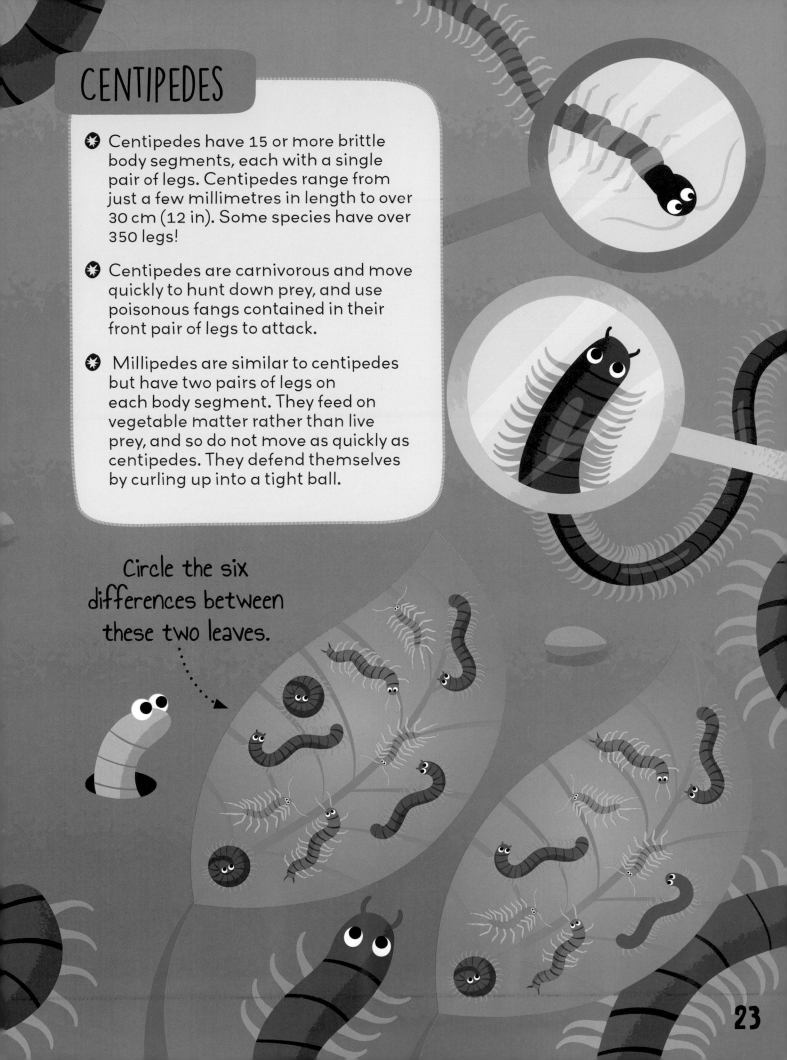

SNAILS AND SLUGS

Snails and slugs are some of the slowest animals on the planet. They ooze slime from their 'foot', which enables them to move safely across both rough and sharp surfaces. They can even travel safely along the blade of a knife. The slime makes them difficult to hold on to. Predators are also deterred by the slime's foul taste.

SIMILARITIES

✷ Snails and slugs don't have legs; they creep very slowly along on an expanding and contracting muscular foot that is protected by their slime.

✷ Both have two pairs of stalk-like tentacles: the upper pair for seeing and the lower pair for smelling.

✷ They have a serrated tongue for ripping at food, such as plants, flowers and vegetables.

✷ They can smell the chemicals in their slime trails, which helps them to track their path home.

Shorter tentacles for smelling

Stalk-like tentacles for seeing

Coiled shell

Muscular foot

Find the stickers to complete the images.

Moist upper surface

Leaves slime trail

DIFFERENCES

✷ A snail has a coiled shell on its back. It can withdraw its whole body into this for protection.

✷ Because it does not have a shell, a slug is more at risk from predators and tries to resist attack by sticking firmly to whatever surface it's on.

✷ The slug is also prone to drying out, which is why it hides away when it's dry and is more active after rain.

DID YOU KNOW?

A female slug can produce up to 90,000 children and grandchildren in her lifetime.

GIANT AFRICAN LAND SNAIL

Found: East Africa

Length: Up to 38 cm (15 in)

Feeds on: Plants, fruit, vegetables

Fun fact:
The world's biggest snail, the giant African land snail can weigh as much as a small chicken (1.3 kg/2.9 lb).

Follow the slime trails to find out which food each snail is going to nibble.

BUG PUZZLES

Let's see what you have learned about bugs and creepy crawlies.

Find the glow-in-the-dark stickers to complete the images.

1. LEGS

How many legs does an insect have?

....

2. INSECTS

Spiders, worms and snails are not insects.

TRUE .... ☐

FALSE .... ☐

3. WINGS

How many pairs of wings does a beetle have?

....

4. PROBOSCIS

What do butterflies use their proboscis for?

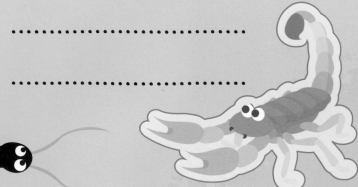

....

....

....

Answers: 1. 6; 2. True; 3. 2; 4. To suck nectar from deep within flowers; 5. False; 6. B) Serrated tongue; 7. C) Grasshoppers rub their back legs against their wings and crickets rub their wings together 8. In its tail.

26

5. LONELY BEES

Bees are very solitary insects, usually living on their own.

TRUE ....☐

FALSE...............☐

6. SNAIL SNACK

How do slugs and snails tear up their food?

A) Big sharp teeth
B) Serrated tongue
C) Electric blender

7. SWEET MUSIC

Which insect makes songs by rubbing its wings together?

A) Spiders
B) Grasshoppers
C) Crickets

8. VENOM

Where does a scorpion store its venom?

....

Now check the answers and see how you did!

I got 7–8 questions right.	**I got 4–6 questions right.**	**I got 0–3 questions right.**
Brilliant. You are the ruler of all the bugs!	Really good. Check which creepy crawlies caught you out.	Good try! You just need a bit more time with this book, or in the garden with your magnifying glass! Then try again later.

BUG LIFE CYCLES

Nearly all bugs lay eggs, which then hatch into babies. But what happens during the life cycle of these creatures when the babies change into adult bugs? It's a process called **metamorphosis**, and there are two forms: **incomplete metamorphosis** and **complete metamorphosis**.

INCOMPLETE METAMORPHOSIS

Bugs such as dragonflies, grasshoppers, spiders, worms, centipedes and snails all go through **incomplete metamorphosis** when changing from a baby to an adult. As babies, they slightly resemble an adult. As they grow bigger, they regularly shed their hard exterior skin to fit their growing body.

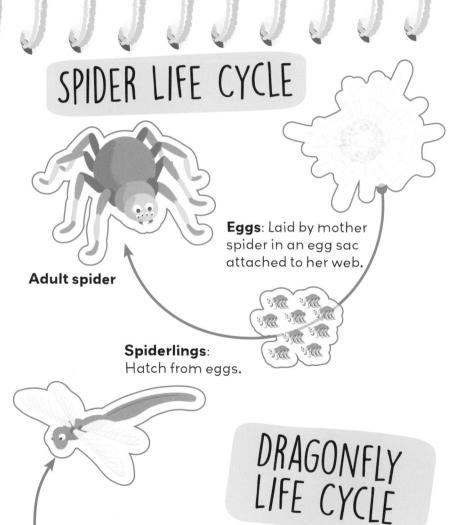

SPIDER LIFE CYCLE

Adult spider

Eggs: Laid by mother spider in an egg sac attached to her web.

Spiderlings: Hatch from eggs.

DRAGONFLY LIFE CYCLE

Adult: The nymph sheds its hard skin up to 15 times as it grows bigger. Under its very last skin, it grows wings. When it sheds this skin, it emerges as an adult dragonfly!

Nymph: No wings but body resembles adult's.

Egg

COMPLETE METAMORPHOSIS

Beetles, butterflies, bees, ants and flies all go through **complete metamorphosis** when changing from baby to adult. With this life cycle, the larva that hatches from the egg looks very different from the adult. For example, a butterfly larva (caterpillar) is like a small worm – very different from an adult butterfly. The larva only looks like an adult butterfly after it has grown a hard skin (called a **pupa**) and completely transformed itself deep within that skin.

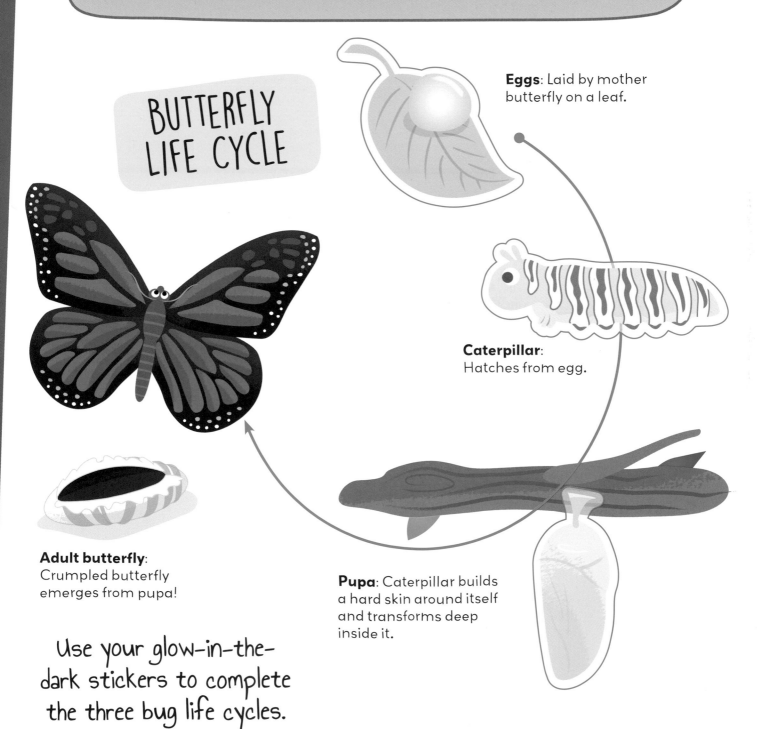

BUTTERFLY LIFE CYCLE

Eggs: Laid by mother butterfly on a leaf.

Caterpillar: Hatches from egg.

Pupa: Caterpillar builds a hard skin around itself and transforms deep inside it.

Adult butterfly: Crumpled butterfly emerges from pupa!

Use your glow-in-the-dark stickers to complete the three bug life cycles.

BUG HOMES

Bugs have many different types of home. Many are very simple: within the hole of a tree, on a plant or even in a shed. But some bugs, especially those living in large colonies, build themselves intricate nests with lots of rooms and passages – almost like miniature versions of our own homes!

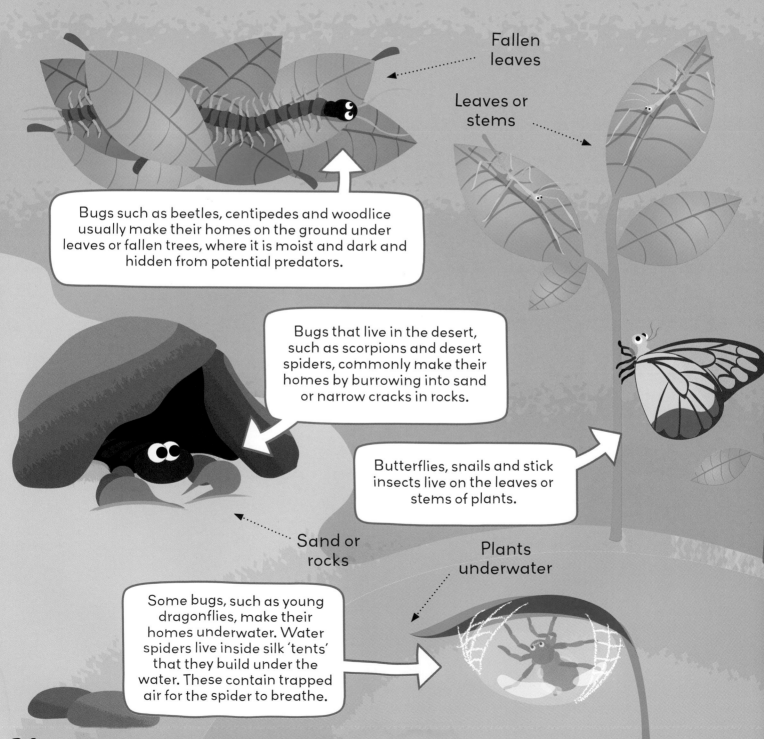

Fallen leaves

Leaves or stems

Bugs such as beetles, centipedes and woodlice usually make their homes on the ground under leaves or fallen trees, where it is moist and dark and hidden from potential predators.

Bugs that live in the desert, such as scorpions and desert spiders, commonly make their homes by burrowing into sand or narrow cracks in rocks.

Butterflies, snails and stick insects live on the leaves or stems of plants.

Sand or rocks

Plants underwater

Some bugs, such as young dragonflies, make their homes underwater. Water spiders live inside silk 'tents' that they build under the water. These contain trapped air for the spider to breathe.

BUGS' NESTS

Ants, bees, wasps and termites all build nests that they share with thousands of others. An ants' nest is made by the ants digging out tunnels under the ground, while bees make their nests by secreting layers of wax in caves or tree hollows. Wasps' nests are made from chewed-up wood or from mud. If you are looking for the most spectacular bugs' nest, it is built by the African termite. The nest itself is underground, but above it the termites construct a huge ventilating tower made of mud. These towers can be as high as 10 m (32 ft).

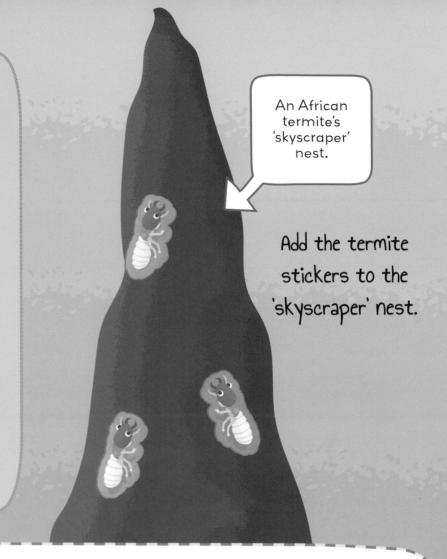

An African termite's 'skyscraper' nest.

Add the termite stickers to the 'skyscraper' nest.

Draw a line from each bug to its correct home.

BUG DEFENCES

Many types of bug might look unappealing to us, but for a lot of small animals they're a delicious meal! Birds, reptiles, fish, bats and even other insects all prey on bugs. So, bugs need a form of defence. Some have painful stings or bites, while others just pretend that they have. Some make themselves very hard to see, while others have bright, scary colours that they deliberately want predators to see.

SESIIDAE MOTH

Found: Worldwide

Length: Up to 0.3 cm (1 in)

Predators: Birds, bats

Fun fact:
Also known as clearwing moth, this mimic bug has yellow and black stripes that make it look like a deadly hornet.

MIMIC BUGS

Some bugs do not have stings or fangs: instead, they mimic bugs that do have them to deceive predators. These bugs look so like the ones they are mimicking that you must get very close to tell the difference, and most predators don't dare.

OWL BUTTERFLY

Found: South America

Length: Up to 2 cm (0.8 in)

Predators: Birds, frogs, lizards

Fun fact:
Active at dusk, this butterfly warns off predators by flashing the spots on its wings so they look like the scary eyes of an owl.

METALMARK MOTH

Found: South-east Asia, Australia

Wingspan: Up to 2 cm (0.8 in)

Predators: Spiders, birds

Fun fact:
When it brings its wings together, this moth looks like a beady-eyed spider and can even save itself from being eaten, as it fools spiders into thinking it is one of their own!

STINGING BUGS

Many bugs use stings or bites to not just kill their prey but to also defend themselves against predators. Not all venomous bugs inject their venom. Some spit it or squirt it at their attackers.

MADAGASCAN FIRE MILLIPEDE

Found: South Africa

Length: 15 cm (6 in)

Predators: Snails, birds, meerkats

Fun fact:
This millipede defends itself by rolling up into a ball and squirting toxic chemicals that burn the predator's skin.

HORNET

Found: Northern hemisphere

Length: 5 cm (2 in)

Predators: Birds, moths, dragonflies

Fun fact:
In Germany, hornets are protected from pest-controllers because of the insect's important role in the ecosystem.

SCARY BUGS

Some bugs actually want to be seen. Their bright colours act as a warning to predators. For example, a wasp's yellow and black stripes warn predators that it stings, and a ladybird's red back warns that it does not taste nice. Some bugs only reveal their bright colours or special markings suddenly, so they shock predators and scare them away.

CAMOUFLAGED BUGS

For very vulnerable bugs, like slow-moving beetles or moths that sleep during the day, camouflage is often the best defence. Camouflaged bugs have colours and markings that are very similar to the plant or tree they are resting on, so that they are hard to see against their background.

THORN BUG

Found: South America, Asia

Length: 1.3 cm (0.5 in)

Feeds on: Plant sap

Fun fact:
Birds and other predators steer clear of this bug. It has a large defensive spike on its back that looks just like a thorn on a twig or branch.

Match the stickers to the bug silhouettes.

NIGHT-TIME BUGS

Take a torch into a garden or wood at night and you'll be surprised how many bugs are crawling or flying around. There are fewer predators at night, so this is the time when many bugs prefer to do their own hunting. Night-time bugs include moths, earthworms, snails, centipedes and various species of beetle and spider.

Glow worms: The larvae (early form) of various beetles, these bugs glow both to attract prey and to warn predators that they are poisonous.

Green lacewing: Unlike most nectar-feeding bugs, the green lacewing hovers around flowers after dark.

Giant centipede: This huge centipede from Australia can stretch to over 16 cm (6 ¼ in) and is only seen at night.

Nightcrawler earthworm: This creature stays underground during the day but crawls around above ground after dark.

Moths: Nearly all moths are nocturnal fliers.

Fireflies: The female of this small flying-beetle species flashes light from her lower body to attract males.

Mosquitoes: Most mosquitoes only feed at night. Only female mosquitoes suck blood, which they use to nourish their eggs.

Yellow ghost spider: This is also known as the garden ghost spider, found in the US and Canada. It hides during the day but comes out to hunt for prey at night.

Snails: Cautious snails only graze at night when there are fewer birds around to prey on them.

Add glow-in-the-dark stickers to complete the scene.

CLEVER BUGS

It is easy to think that bugs, being so small, are not as intelligent as other animals. But many bugs prove themselves to be quite clever in the way they build their homes, hunt for food and defend themselves. And some species are extremely clever...

HONEYBEES

Found: Worldwide except in very cold regions such as Antarctica.

Length: 1.2 cm (0.5 in)

Feeds on: Nectar and pollen

Probably the cleverest type of bug of all, honeybees are able to learn and memorise. This means they come to know the best way to reach the nectar for each type of flower. Even more amazingly, honeybees can convey the knowledge they gain to other honeybees. They do this by a series of movements called a 'waggle dance'. These dances tell other bees the location and distance of good plants for nectar.

LEAF-CUTTER ANTS

Found: South America

Length: Up to 1.6 cm (0.6 in)

Feeds on: Leaf fungus

All species of ants are clever, but the leaf-cutter ant is the cleverest of all of them. Their underground nests are like huge hotels, full of long passages and hundreds of chambers. Their nests even have special 'gardens' where they grow their food. Troops of leaf-cutter ants bring nibbled leaves back to the nest, which are used as fungus in the gardens. The fungus can provide food for as many as eight million ants in the nest.

DIVING BELL SPIDER

Found: Europe

Length: Up to 1.68 cm (0.7 in)

Like all spiders, the diving bell spider needs air to live; but it spends most of its time under the water. So how does it get its oxygen? While it spends very little time out of the water, during that time, the diving bell spider traps air between the hairs on its body and legs. Back under the water, it makes a special balloon-shaped web to hold the trapped air and lives there, only scuttling out to catch prey and then retreating back inside.

DUNG BEETLE

Found: Worldwide

Length: Up to 3 cm (1.8 in)

Feeds on: Dung

Dung beetles are the first known species to be able to navigate by using the stars. They follow the bright stripe of light from the Milky Way, which helps them to move in a straight line – without this light to guide them, they just roll about.

Find the stickers to complete the images.

CICADA

Found: Worldwide

Length: Up to 5 cm (2 in)

Feeds on: Sap from various trees

What makes the cicada a clever bug? It uses its loud clicking sound as an alarm system! By rapidly vibrating its external skeleton, its largely hollow body acts like a drum, amplifying the vibrations. It can warn other cicadas of danger from as far away as 1 km (0.6 miles). This sound can also be used to attract females.

WEIRD BUGS

You may think many bugs look strange, with their large bulbous eyes or their unusual camouflage. A few, however, are especially weird in their appearance or their behaviour. Here are some of the weirdest!

PRAYING MANTIS

Found: Tropical regions

Length: Up to 15 cm (6 in)

Feeds on: Crickets, moths and flies

The praying mantis gets its name from its pose when resting, as it resembles a person at prayer. With its triangular head and bulging eyes, the praying mantis looks more like an alien than a bug. It can even turn its head 180 degrees, so it can peer at you over its shoulder!

Use your glow-in-the-dark stickers to reveal one of the world's weirdest bugs.

FLIC-FLAC SPIDER

Found: Deserts in Morocco

Length: Up to 2 cm (0.75 in)

Feeds on: Moths

Ever seen a spider doing cartwheels? The flic-flac spider does! When threatened, the flic-flac spider, instead of scampering away, leaps into the air and does a series of quick somersaults and flips to escape.

HUMMINGBIRD HAWK-MOTH

Found: Europe, Asia

Length: Up to 6 cm (2.4 in)

Feeds on: Flower nectar

Like the hummingbird, this moth has a long thin bill for reaching deep inside flowers to drink their nectar. It hovers almost stationary next to a flower by flapping its wings very fast, just like a hummingbird.

WORM-SNAILS

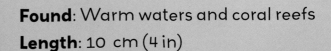

Found: Warm waters and coral reefs

Length: 10 cm (4 in)

Feeds on: Marine micro-organisms

A unique snail that cements itself to a rock and never moves again! Instead of having a coiled shell, the snail-worm grows a long tube-like shell. It has an extra pair of tentacles, like arms, and, just like Spider-man, it shoots out a web. Micro-organisms get stuck in the web, which the worm-snail then eats.

BEAUTIFUL BUGS

People often think bugs are ugly, but many are considered beautiful. There are some butterflies, bees, grasshoppers and even spiders that are as magnificent as any other animal on Earth.

ALEXANDRA'S BIRD WING

Found: Papua New Guinea

Wingspan: Up to 30 cm (12 in)

Feeds on: Vine nectar

This is not just the world's largest butterfly: it is also one of the most spectacular. Its size and beauty make it highly appealing to butterfly collectors, which is why it is a criminal offence to catch one, as they are endangered.

Add some glow-in-the-dark Orchid Bee stickers!

GOLDEN ORB WEAVER SPIDER

Found: Australia

Length: Up to 13 cm (5 in)

Feeds on: Flies, beetles, even small birds

The golden orb weaver has a green or red body with black and orange striped legs. It is not just the spider itself that is stunning; it also produces a beautiful web with yellow threads that shimmer like gold in the sunlight, giving the spider its name.

ORCHID BEE

Found: Central America   **Length:** Up to 1.4 cm (0.5 in)

Feeds on: Pollen, nectar

This species comes in a stunning range of metallic colours: blues, greens, reds and gold, making the bees look like flying jewels. Not only does the male orchid bee look exotic, it smells magnificent too. To attract females, it collects special scents from flowers, converting them into an exotic perfume.

Which of these four bugs do you think is the most attractive? Draw it here and add small bugs for decoration.

RAINBOW GRASSHOPPER

Found: Deserts of USA and Mexico

Length: Up to 3.5 cm (1.4 in)

Feeds on: Grasses

This stunning grasshopper is also called a painted grasshopper because it looks as though someone has painted it with bright, thick acrylic paints. The rainbow grasshopper's black head, body and legs are covered with red, yellow and blue stripes and markings. All those pretty colours are not to make the grasshopper look attractive, though they're to scare away predators!

VILE BUGS

Meet some of the world's most vile bugs. You may be fascinated by the places they inhabit and the disgusting things they eat, but beware! Some bugs can live inside your body, some feed on your blood or nutrients inside your body and others can pass on dangerous germs!

TAPEWORM

Found: Worldwide

Length: Up to 30 m (100 ft)

Feeds on: Food inside your body

This worm lives inside the stomach of animals and humans. It uses its many suckers and hooks to attach itself to the lining of your intestines, and then eats the food that passes over it. It can reach up to 30 m (98 ft) and can stay inside your body for up to 25 years!

HEAD LOUSE

Found: Worldwide

Length: Up to 0.3 cm (0.12 in)

Feeds on: Blood and skin

These tiny bugs grip your hair with their long claws, then suck blood from your scalp. The good news is that they only live for a month. The bad news is that the female can lay up to 300 eggs in your hair during that time.

BROWN STINK BUG

Found: South-east Asia

Length: Up to 1.5 cm (0.5 in)

Feeds on: Fruit and vegetables

These home-loving bugs release a foul odour when threatened or crushed. They don't like the cold, they make their way inside houses and then release a different, more chemical odour which acts as an invitation to other stink bugs to join them. There can be thousands in just one house hibernating throughout winter.

Place each vile-bug sticker on top of the thing it likes most.

SLUG

Found: Worldwide

Length: Up to 20 cm (8 in)

Feeds on: Vegetable and flower leaves

Some slugs just nibble the vegetables in your garden, but some feed on vile things like rat poo. This can cause serious diseases if you accidentally eat a slug in your salad!

COCKROACH

Found: Worldwide

Length: Up to 8 cm (3.25 in)

Feeds on: Decaying food

These despised bugs transfer all sorts of serious germs from dirty places like sewers to kitchens, where they scavenge at night for spilt food. They will even eat the wax inside your ear – or the toothpaste left on your toothbrush!

DEADLY BUGS

They might be very small, but some bugs are as deadly as the world's most dangerous mammals or reptiles. These killer bugs have bites or stings that can be fatal, not just to other animals, but also to humans.

SYDNEY FUNNEL WEB SPIDER

Find the stickers to complete the images.

Found: Eastern Australia

Length: Up to 15 cm (6 in)

Feeds on: Frogs, lizards, mice

Probably the world's deadliest spider, the Sydney funnel web spider clings on to its victim, stinging them repeatedly. Its poisonous fangs are so sharp, they can even penetrate tough leather shoes, and its lethal venom destroys the body's nervous system, causing death in as little as 15 minutes.

JAPANESE GIANT HORNET

Found: Japan

Length: Up to 4.5 cm (1.8 in)

Feeds on: Large insects, tree sap

This lethal hornet causes up to 40 deaths a year. It has a very long stinger that injects a large amount of deadly venom. You can try running away, but it's attracted by human sweat and will pursue you even more!

FIRE ANT

Found: South America

Length: Up to 0.6 cm (0.25 in)

Feeds on: Young plants, seeds

Causing up to 12 human deaths a year, this deadly ant gets its name from its sting, which feels like red-hot fire. It attacks by gripping with its bite and then using its stinger to inject its fiery venom.

INDIAN RED SCORPION

Found: India

Length: Up to 9 cm (3.5 in)

Feeds on: Insects, lizards

Recognised as the the world's deadliest scorpion, this small scorpion has a very large stinger. Its deadly venom proves fatal in over 30% of attacks on humans.

MOSQUITOES

Found: Worldwide

Length: Up to 0.9 cm (0.35 in)

Feeds on: Flowers (males), blood (females)

Far and away, the deadliest of all bugs in the whole animal kingdom is the mosquito. A male mosquito feeds on flowers but the female mosquito sucks animal or human blood to get nutrients for her eggs, piercing the skin with a pair of needle-like mouthparts. She often carries deadly diseases, like malaria: according to the World Health Organization, mosquito bites result in the deaths of up to 1 million people every year. Vaccinations against mosquito-borne illnesses are vital before travelling.

RECORD BREAKERS

All these bugs are record breakers!
Find the glow-in-the-dark stickers to fill the spaces.

Name: Goliath beetle
Found: Africa
Length: Up to 11 cm (4.3 in)
Fab fact: The larvae is even larger than the adult goliath beetle: up to twice its length and weight!

WORLD'S LARGEST INSECT

WORLD'S HEAVIEST INSECT

Name: Giant weta
Found: New Zealand
Length: Up to 10 cm (4 in)
Fab fact: Weighs up to 70 g (2.5 oz) – same as a small bird!

Name: Chinese stick insect
Found: Southern China
Diet: Leaves
Fab fact: It can be as long as 62 cm (24.5 in) – the length of an average person's arm!

WORLD'S LONGEST INSECT

WORLD'S LONGEST EARTHWORM

Name: African giant earthworm
Found: Africa
Weight: Up to 1.5 kg (3.3 lb)
Fab fact: Can measure up to 6.7 m (22 ft) long – that's about five times your height!

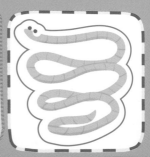

Name: Goliath bird-eating spider
Found: South America
Length: Up to 12 cm (4.7 in)
Fab fact: Birds are not the only thing it eats – it likes large frogs, lizards and even rodents and snakes!

WORLD'S LONGEST SPIDER

46

Name: Hercules beetle
Found: South America
Length: Up to 17.5 cm (7 in)
Fab fact: Can carry up to 850 times its body weight!

Name: Southern giant darner dragonfly
Found: Australia
Length: Up to 12.7 cm (5 in)
Fab fact: Can travel up to 96km/hr (60m/hr) – the same as a speeding car!

Name: Tiger beetle
Found: South America, Australia
Length: Up to 4.5 cm (1.8 in)
Fab fact: Can reach speeds of up to 9 km/hr (5.6 m/hr) – the speed of an average jogger!

Make up your very own record-breaking bug. Draw its body parts and give stats showing where it is found and what makes it a record breaker.

Name: ....

Found: ....

Length: ....

Fab fact: ....

....

47

BUG QUIZ

1. What is the larva of a butterfly called?

....

2. In which organs does a scorpion's sting cause fatal paralysis?

A) The stomach and liver
B) The heart and lungs
C) The small and large intestines

3. Why does a honeybee do a 'waggle dance'?

....

....

4. Which bug makes the loudest sound?

....

5. Which is the world's deadliest bug?

....

6. What type of spider will do cartwheels to escape from danger?

....

Reward yourself with stickers as you go!

I got 7–8 questions right.
Brilliant! You are a top bug expert!

I got 4–6 questions right.
Well done! Now try going back over the bugs you weren't so sure about.

I got 0–3 questions right.
Don't let those creepy crawlies defeat you! Read over these pages, then try again later.

Answers: 1. Caterpillar **2.** B) The heart and lungs **3.** To let other honeybees know where to find nectar **4.** Cicada **5.** Mosquito **6.** The flic-flac spider